Grandma Millie's Workshop

ISBN 979-8-88685-895-2 (paperback)
ISBN 979-8-88685-897-6 (hardcover)
ISBN 979-8-88685-896-9 (digital)

Christian Faith Publishing
832 Park Avenue
Meadville, PA 16335
www.christianfaithpublishing.com

Printed in the United States of America

Grandma Millie's Workshop

WRITTEN BY: PAULA PETREE

ILLUSTRATED BY: KAREN TRYBONE

Grandma Millie's workshop is a place I remember fondly from my childhood. I can recall so vividly the sights, smells, and sounds of that wonderful place. The fragrant scents of gardenias and lilacs wafting in the air; the beautiful vibrant hues of blue, pink, yellow, and red tickling my eyes; the inviting sound of Grandma Millie's voice lovingly speaking kind words to an eager pair of ears. I can close my eyes at this very moment, and I am right back there in that beautiful place reliving all of those beautiful memories.

When I was a girl, I spent many happy hours there in that workshop and in the garden behind the workshop with my grandma. At the sound of the last bell of school, I ran as fast as I could to her workshop. She was always there waiting for me to burst through the door. Long hugs and talks about the day followed. Then I would help Grandma Millie with whatever she was doing: planting, weeding, cutting, or arranging flowers.

Sometimes we were in her workshop, and sometimes we were in her beautiful garden.

Grandma Millie was happiest when she was working with her flowers. She would often hum. Maybe a familiar song, maybe not a song at all, but her humming was happy and cheerful.

Grandma Millie had a talent for flowers. Not only could she grow them, but she could create beautiful arrangements with her flowers, selecting just the right combination of flowers from her lush garden. Cutting, arranging, fluffing, standing back with a critical eye, and evaluating until...*just right*!

When an arrangement was finished, Grandma Millie would deliver it to just the person or place that needed it. Sometimes it was the church down the street. The beautiful old cathedral was open most days for prayer. She would place the flowers, just so, in a way that made her smile.

After placing her beautiful flowers on the altar table, she would say a quick prayer before heading back home. When people saw the flowers, they knew who had put them there.

7

Sometimes Grandma Millie hand-delivered her flower creations to a friend who was sick or going through a hard time. Other times she would take a flower arrangement to an acquaintance who needed something good and beautiful in her life.

When Grandma Millie would show up with one of her fabulous creations, it was sure to cheer even the saddest of people. Handing the flower arrangement to someone always brought smiles, which led to laughter and probably a heartfelt hug.

Sometimes I had the privilege of tagging along with Grandma Millie as she delivered her flowers. It seemed a simple gesture, but what grand results! I learned that simply taking time to do kind things for people can make a huge difference in the lives of others. I can remember that feeling of satisfaction and fulfillment realizing that such a small act could have such lasting results.

As a girl, I loved being in Grandma Millie's workshop. It was warm and cozy and always cheerful. The shelves all along the wall were lined with the tools of her trade—scissors, pruners, watering cans, vases, baskets, ribbons, and other necessary instruments for her work. Next to the door were the gardening tools: shovel, rake, and wheelbarrow. To the left of her workshop was her work bench where the magic happened.

Windows adorned the perimeter of the room allowing ample lighting for her work. It wasn't grand or fancy in any way, but it was my absolute favorite place in the entire world.

When I was very young, I had to stand on tiptoe just to see what was going on.

Watching Grandma Millie work arranging flowers was calming to me. Sometimes she smiled, sometimes she hummed softly, and sometimes she talked to me while working—all the while patiently creating, removing, re-arranging, and starting again over and over until it was just right.

She had an eye for all things beautiful and the ability to make it happen.

The conversations we had were nothing at all, yet looking back, they were everything to a little girl. The things Grandma Millie and I shared in her workshop helped shape who I am today. I learned the art of patience and kindness. I learned that doing things for others was very satisfying. I learned what it means to work at something, undo it, and start over again without giving up. I learned to have patience with myself and to trust my instincts. I learned to pay attention to details—not to miss the little things. I learned satisfaction in doing something worthwhile. Yes, I learned a lot from Grandma Millie.

I also learned the art and love of gardening and flower arranging. I am no longer a young girl, and Grandma Millie is no longer here on this earth, but she is with me every single moment of every single day. I don't have a workshop as Grandma Millie did all those years ago, but I am content with what I have—another lesson I learned in Grandma Millie's workshop. Who knows, maybe I can teach a certain someone a thing or two!

About the Author

Paula Petree is a retired kindergarten teacher. She taught for twenty-eight years in a little town in Kentucky where she and her husband raised their two children. Upon retiring, they moved to the mountains of East Tennessee where they now reside. Paula enjoys reading, writing, and listening to music.

Karen Trybone is also a retired teacher. She taught middle school students in Tennessee for thirty-five years. Karen now lives in the Great Smoky Mountains of East Tennessee where she enjoys drawing, painting, and listening to music.